THE BLESSINGS OF MY LIFE

A MOTHER'S RECORD BOOK

© 2000 Havoc Publishing
San Diego, California 92121
U.S.A.

Artwork By Linda Spivey
Artwork © 2000 under license from Penny Lane Publishing, Inc.
Text by Jill Lemming

ISBN 1-57977-167-X

www.havocpub.com

Made in Korea

THE BLESSINGS OF MY LIFE

This book lovingly
records the life of:

A PERFECT GIFT TO CHERISH
THIS BLESSING FROM ABOVE...
OUR BABY SOFT AND GENTLE,
THE LIGHT OF GOD'S OWN LOVE

Photo

Mother

Weight

Father

Length

Name

Date

Time

City, State and Place Where Born

Mother, tell me about when and where you were born

_____

_____

_____

_____

Tell me the story about the name your parents gave you

_____

_____

_____

_____

What events happened the year you were born? _____

_____

_____

_____

_____

_____

_____

Mother, tell me about your mother: her full name, where she was born, where she grew up. Do you know any interesting stories about her? _____

_____

_____

_____

_____

_____

What are your favorite memories of her? _____

_____

_____

_____

_____

_____

Photo of your

Mother

_____

Tell me about your father: his full name, where he was born, where he grew up. Do you know any interesting stories about him? What are your favorite memories of him?

_____

_____

_____

_____

_____

_____

_____

_____

Photo of your

Father

_____

_____

_____

_____

_____

_____

Photographs

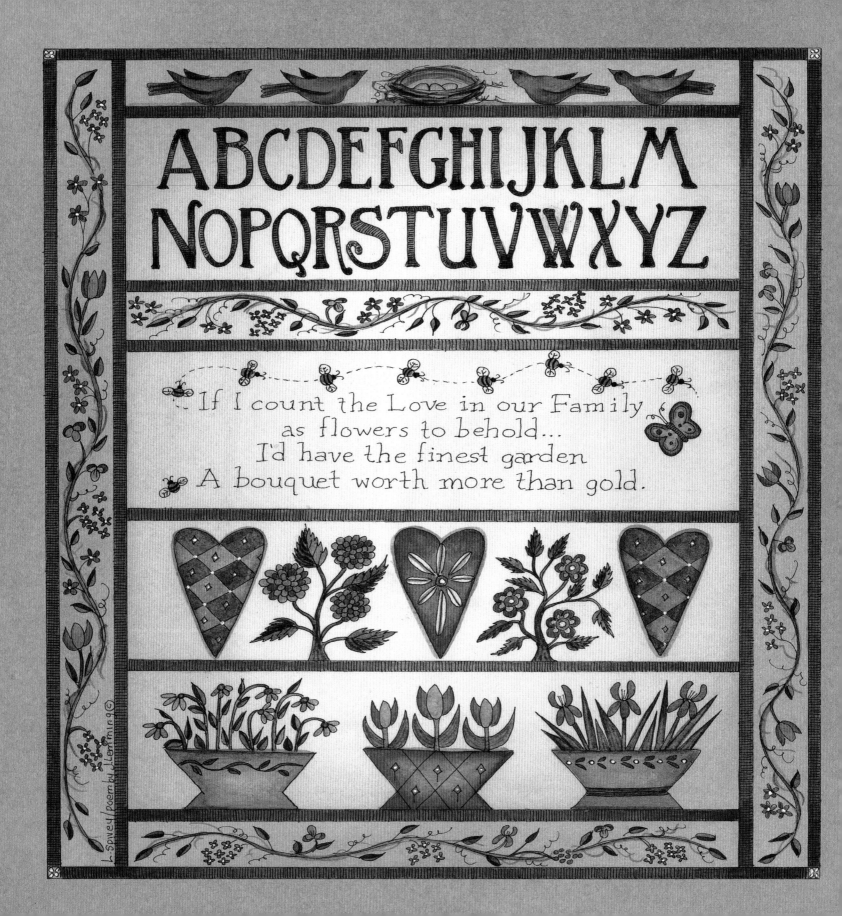

Tell me about your family, about your brothers and sisters: their full names, where they were born, and their birth dates. _____

_____

_____

_____

_____

_____

Did you share a room with anyone? Any interesting stories about growing up with them? _____

_____

_____

What are your favorite memories of them? _____

_____

_____

_____

_____

_____

_____

L. Spivey/poem by J.Lemming©

Mother, I want to know about your grandparents. What are their full names, where were they born, and what do you remember about them?

Your mother's mother: _____

_____

_____

_____

_____

_____

_____

_____

Your mother's father: _____

_____

_____

_____

_____

_____

_____

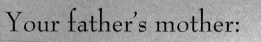

Your father's mother: _____

_____
_____
_____
_____
_____
_____

Your father's father: _____

_____
_____
_____
_____
_____
_____
_____
_____
_____

Photographs

So much love to spread around
why keep it locked inside...
Love is meant for sharing,
not to store away and hide.

SO MUCH LOVE TO SPREAD AROUND
WHY KEEP IT LOCKED INSIDE...
LOVE IS MEANT FOR SHARING,
NOT TO STORE AWAY AND HIDE.

Mother, share some favorite memories of your childhood

_____
_____
_____
_____
_____
_____

Share stories you heard as a child. _____

_____
_____
_____
_____
_____
_____
_____

Spivey / Poem by J. Lemming

WITHIN THE HEART OF OUR FAMILY
THE THREADS OF LOVE ARE SEWN
GENERATIONS BEING BLESSED
BY THE SWEETEST LOVE EVER KNOWN

Mother, tell me about the bedroom you had as a child. How was it special to you? Did you have a special quilt or blanket? Where did it come from? _____

_____

_____

_____

_____

Did you learn to sew or knit? Who taught you? What were some of the things you made? _____

_____

_____

_____

_____

_____

Hobbies you enjoyed as a youth: _____

_____

_____

Hobbies you enjoy now: _____

_____

_____

Tell me, Mother, about some favorite spring-time memories. Did you ever fly a kite, climb a tree or pick wildflowers? Who did these things with you?

_____

_____

_____

_____

_____

_____

_____

Tell me about your childhood home, neighborhood and friends.

_____

_____

_____

_____

_____

_____

_____

Blessings

Bless this special family
and help them, Lord I pray...
Bring them love and laughter
and joy along the way.

What memories do you have, Mother, of going to church as a child? _____

_____

_____

_____

_____

_____

_____

_____

Tell me how you celebrated Easter. Did you color Easter eggs and have Easter egg hunts?

_____

_____

_____

_____

_____

_____

_____

Mother, did you have a favorite doll or stuffed animal or toy? Who gave it to you? What name did you give it? Whatever became of it? _____

_____

_____

_____

_____

_____

_____

What were your favorite games to play as a child? _____

_____

_____

_____

_____

_____

_____

Did you have favorite pets when you were growing up?
Tell me about them. What made them special? Do you
have a funny story about something they did?

Photographs

Mother, what were your favorite activities in the summer? How did you keep cool? Did you go swimming?

_____

_____

_____

_____

_____

Did you ride a bicycle? Where would you ride? _____

_____

_____

_____

_____

Did you ever go camping? _____

_____

_____

_____

Mother, when you were young, what did you do to help in the kitchen? _____

_____

_____

_____

_____

_____

Was your mother a good cook? What kind of food did she fix the most? _____

_____

_____

_____

What else were you expected to do around the house?

_____

_____

_____

_____

Favorite Family Recipes

Favorite Family Recipes

_____

_____

_____

_____

_____

_____

_____

_____

_____

_____

_____

_____

_____

_____

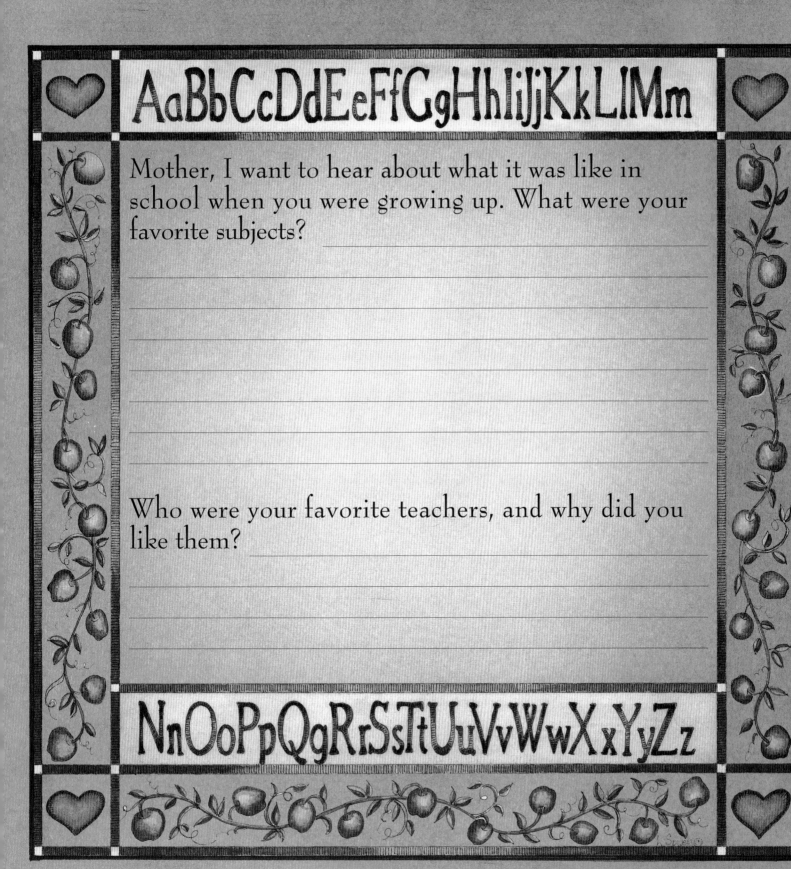

AaBbCcDdEeFfGgHhIiJjKkLlMm

Mother, I want to hear about what it was like in school when you were growing up. What were your favorite subjects?

Who were your favorite teachers, and why did you like them?

NnOoPpQgRrSsTtUuVvWwXxYyZz

Tell me about your favorite school activities.

Tell me about your High School. What year did you graduate and how many were in your graduating class? Tell me about graduation day.

_____

_____

_____

_____

_____

_____

Did you go to a formal dance or prom? Who was your date and what did you wear?

_____

_____

_____

_____

_____

_____

AaBbCcDdEeFfGgHhIiJjKkLlMm

School Pictures

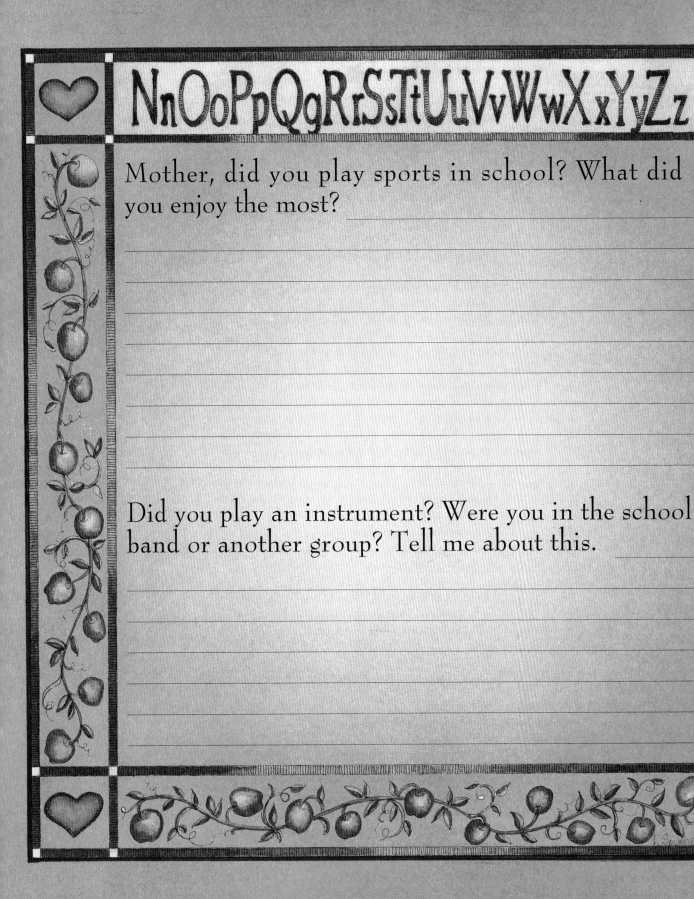

NnOoPpQqRrSsTtUuVvWwXxYyZz

Mother, did you play sports in school? What did you enjoy the most? _____

_____

_____

_____

_____

_____

_____

_____

Did you play an instrument? Were you in the school band or another group? Tell me about this. _____

_____

_____

_____

_____

_____

Good friends are like flowers and their beauty lights the way...
They can lift a lonely spirit and brighten up the day.

Mother, tell me about the friends you had while growing up. What did you do together? _____

_____

_____

_____

_____

_____

_____

_____

_____

_____

_____

_____

_____

_____

_____

_____

_____

_____

AUTUMN'S GREETING

When you were a young girl, Mother, did you go trick-or-treating on Halloween? How did you dress up? Where did you get your costume? _____

_____

_____

_____

_____

_____

Did you carve pumpkins? What kind of face would you carve? _____

_____

_____

_____

What kind of treats did you get? _____

_____

_____

Mother, how did your family celebrate Thanksgiving when you were young? Did you have guests? _____

_____

_____

_____

_____

_____

_____

_____

Who did all the cooking? What was served? _____

_____

_____

_____

_____

_____

_____

Family Gathering Photographs

Family Gathering Photographs

Tell me, Mother, of some favorite Christmas memories. How did your family celebrate the holidays? Did you celebrate Christmas in a religious way?

Tell me about your Christmas tree. How did you decorate it? Did you hang up a stocking for Santa?

_____

_____

_____

_____

_____

What kind of gifts did you give your Mother and Father? Did anyone ever make something special for you?

_____

_____

_____

_____

_____

_____

Dear Santa I have been good

Photographs

Mother, tell me some favorite wintertime memories. What kind of activities did you do? _____

_____

_____

_____

_____

_____

_____

_____

_____

_____

_____

_____

_____

_____

_____

_____

_____

_____

_____

UNITED ON THIS DAY

TWO HEARTS JOINED IN MARRIAGE
IN THE PRESENCE OF THE LORD
EACH HAS MADE A PROMISE
TO LOVE FOREVERMORE

Your Wedding Day

Mother, tell me about your Wedding Day. When and where did you get married? Who performed the ceremony? Who was in your wedding? _____

_____

_____

_____

_____

_____

_____

Did you wear a special dress? Where did you get it?

_____

_____

Did you go on a honeymoon? Where did you go? _____

_____

_____

_____

About Father

Mother, tell me about Father. What is his full name, where and when was he born and where did he grow up? _____

_____
_____
_____
_____

What are the names of his parents? Do you know where they were born and where they grew up?

_____
_____
_____

What are the names of his brothers and sisters?

_____
_____
_____

How old were you, Mother, when you met Father?
What did you first think of him? _____

_____

_____

_____

Tell me about your first home together. What was
the address? How did you furnish it? Do you have
any family heirlooms? Where did they come
from?

_____

_____

_____

_____

_____

_____

_____

Mother, how old were you when you first had children? What were your thoughts as you became a mother? What did Father think?

Photographs

Mother, what are the most important events of your life that have made you the person you are today?

Family Photographs

Spivey /poem by J. Lemming ©

Family Photographs